BEANO.

THE DENNIS COLLECTION

A STUDIO PRESS BOOK

First published in the UK in 2020 by Studio Press,
an imprint of Bonnier Books UK,
The Plaza, 535 King's Road, London SW10 0SZ
Owned by Bonnier Books,
Sveavägen 56, Stockholm, Sweden

studiopressbooks.co.uk
bonnierbooks.co.uk

1 3 5 7 9 10 8 6 4 2

All rights reserved
ISBN 978-1-78741-695-6

Designed by Nia Williams

A CIP catalogue for this book is available from the British Library
Printed and bound in China

BEANO

THE DENNIS COLLECTION

STUDIO PRESS

Forever ten years old, Dennis has never stopped growing in popularity.

This book allows us to experience his growth into a world-famous icon. He's been the cover star of the world's best comic since the year I was born, so I feel like I've shared some of his greatest moments and now I can't wait to relive them.

Dennis began in early 1951 when scriptwriter Ian Chisolm's roughly sketched idea was taken on by artist David "Davey" Law. Ian's ideas and scripts were gratuitously naughty. Dennis tossing fireworks and lit matches down a well to create a 'volcano' was one of his subtler experiments!

Davey's original Dennis design evolved radically and by the mid-fifties he'd undergone a dramatic growth-spurt; symbolic of the character extending his influence in *The Beano*.

Dennis became stockier again in the sixties, with a looser art style, featuring low horizons that evoked the world from a kid's point of view. This enabled readers to feel they were there alongside Dennis, participating in mischief vicariously.

Fellow former Beano editor Euan Kerr told me how he once met Davey, and witnessed him repeatedly scrubbing out what appeared to be completed drawings, searching for perfection. This attitude has been shared by every Dennis artist since.

Continual micro-enhancements are why Dennis has stood the test of time. Beano scriptwriters have ensured he has always reflected the lives of kids in the here and now. Dennis has never stood still. He's a bespoke inspiration for every generation.

'My' Dennis was drawn by David Sutherland. Dave drew Dennis throughout my era as a paying Beano reader, and I've been privileged to since work with him. He's an exception to the rule that warns against meeting your heroes.

He actually 'ghosted' Davey Law's Dennis regularly from the late sixties and, so closely did he emulate the style, it's almost impossible to tell their work apart - especially since artists' signatures didn't appear on their work at that time.

Dave became the full-time Dennis artist in 1971. This was in addition to his weekly Bash Street Kids strip, so it was no surprise Beano fans celebrated him as the comic's star artist. Such is his modesty, Dave will probably be surprised to read that statement.

I feel it was his amazing development of Gnasher (first drawn by Law in August 1968), that helped the overall popularity of Dennis grow stronger. Gnasher is so well known nowadays we forget how radical it was to present an ostensibly scruffy dog… with a suavely 'clean-shaven' face. Genius.

In 1998, David Parkins became the third David to draw Dennis, introducing Dennis's baby sister, Bea. A who's who of amazing artists have followed, with Jim Hansen, Barrie Appleby and Tam Paterson all becoming particular favourites of some kid, somewhere, at some time.

The indefatigable Nigel Parkinson has brought Dennis to life brilliantly since my own Beano editorship. He always adds 'just one more thing' for his reader to enjoy. With scripts from the hilarious Nigel Auchterlounie this guarantees Dennis will continue to grow forever. No wonder he's the world's biggest comic star.

I hope you find your own favourite Dennis in the pages to come.

Mike Stirling
Editorial Director
Beano Studios

DENNIS THE MENACE

MARCH 17th, 1951

DENNIS THE MENACE

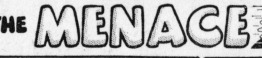

MAY 5th, 1951

PRINTED AND PUBLISHED IN GREAT BRITAIN BY D C THOMSON & CO. LTD., AND JOHN LENG & CO., LTD 12 FETTER LANE, FLEET STREET, LONDON. E.C.4. REGISTERED FOR TRANSMISSION BY CANADIAN MAGAZINE POST.

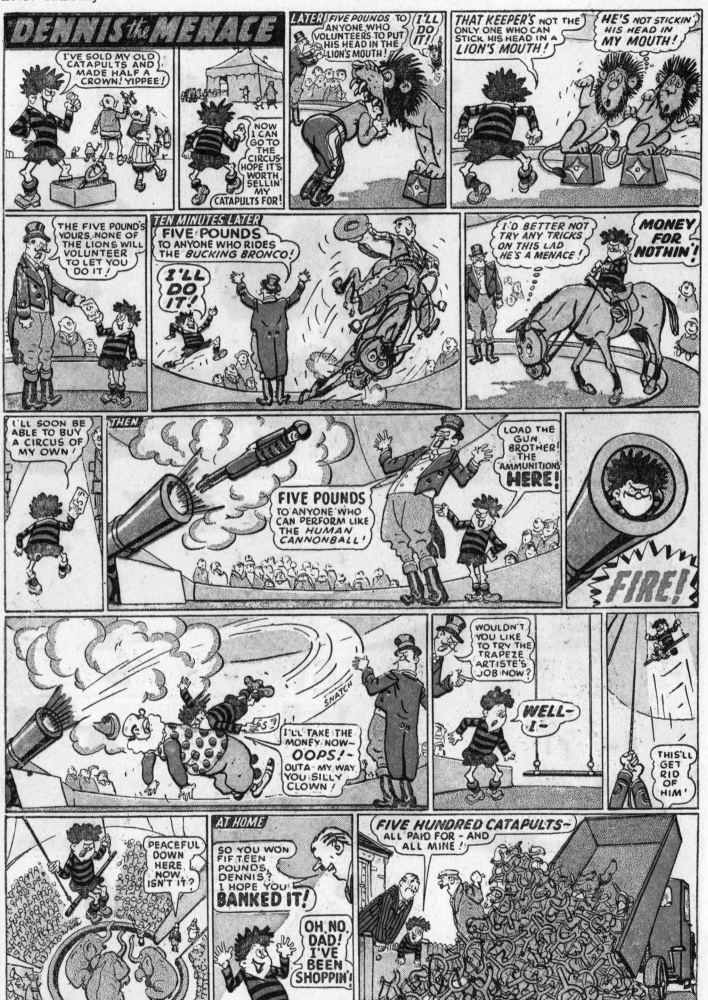

PRINTED AND PUBLISHED IN GREAT BRITAIN BY D. C. THOMSON & CO., LTD., AND JOHN LENG & CO. LTD. 12 FETTER LANE, FLEET STREET, LONDON, E.C.4. REGISTERED FOR TRANSMISSION BY CANADIAN MAGAZINE POST.

PRINTED AND PUBLISHED IN GREAT BRITAIN BY D. C. THOMSON & CO. LTD. AND JOHN LENG & CO. LTD. 12 FETTER LANE, FLEET STREET, LONDON E.C.4. REGISTERED FOR TRANSMISSION BY CANADIAN MAGAZINE POST.

PRINTED AND PUBLISHED IN GREAT BRITAIN BY D. C. THOMSON & CO., LTD., AND JOHN LENG & CO., LTD., 12 FETTER LANE, FLEET STREET, LONDON, E.C.4. REGISTERED FOR TRANSMISSION BY CANADIAN MAGAZINE POST.

DENNIS the MENACE

PRINTED AND PUBLISHED IN GREAT BRITAIN BY D. C. THOMSON & CO., LTD., AND JOHN LENG & CO., LTD., 12 FETTER LANE, FLEET STREET, LONDON, E.C.4. REGISTERED FOR TRANSMISSION BY CANADIAN MAGAZINE POST.

DENNIS the MENACE

PRINTED AND PUBLISHED IN GREAT BRITAIN BY D. C. THOMSON & CO., LTD., AND JOHN LENG & CO., LTD., 12 FETTER LANE, FLEET STREET, LONDON, E.C.4. REGISTERED FOR TRANSMISSION BY CANADIAN MAGAZINE POST.

DENNIS the MENACE

PRINTED AND PUBLISHED IN GREAT BRITAIN BY D. C. THOMSON & CO. LTD., AND JOHN LENG & CO., LTD., 12 FETTER LANE, FLEET STREET, LONDON, E.C.4. REGISTERED FOR TRANSMISSION BY CANADIAN MAGAZINE POST.

DENNIS the MENACE

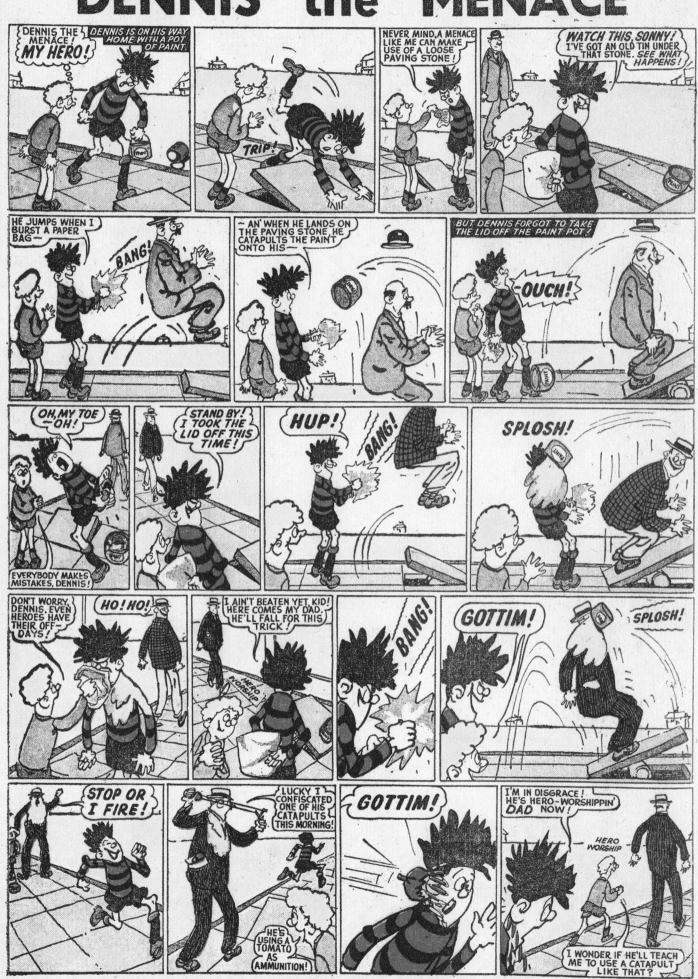

PRINTED AND PUBLISHED IN GREAT BRITAIN BY D. C. THOMSON & CO. LTD. AND JOHN LENG & CO., LTD., 12 FETTER LANE, FLEET STREET, LONDON, E.C.4. REGISTERED FOR TRANSMISSION BY CANADIAN MAGAZINE POST.

DENNIS the MENACE

PRINTED AND PUBLISHED IN GREAT BRITAIN BY D. C. THOMSON & CO., LTD., AND JOHN LENG & CO., LTD., 12 FETTER LANE, FLEET STREET, LONDON, E.C.4. REGISTERED FOR TRANSMISSION BY CANADIAN MAGAZINE POST.

JANUARY 21st, 1961

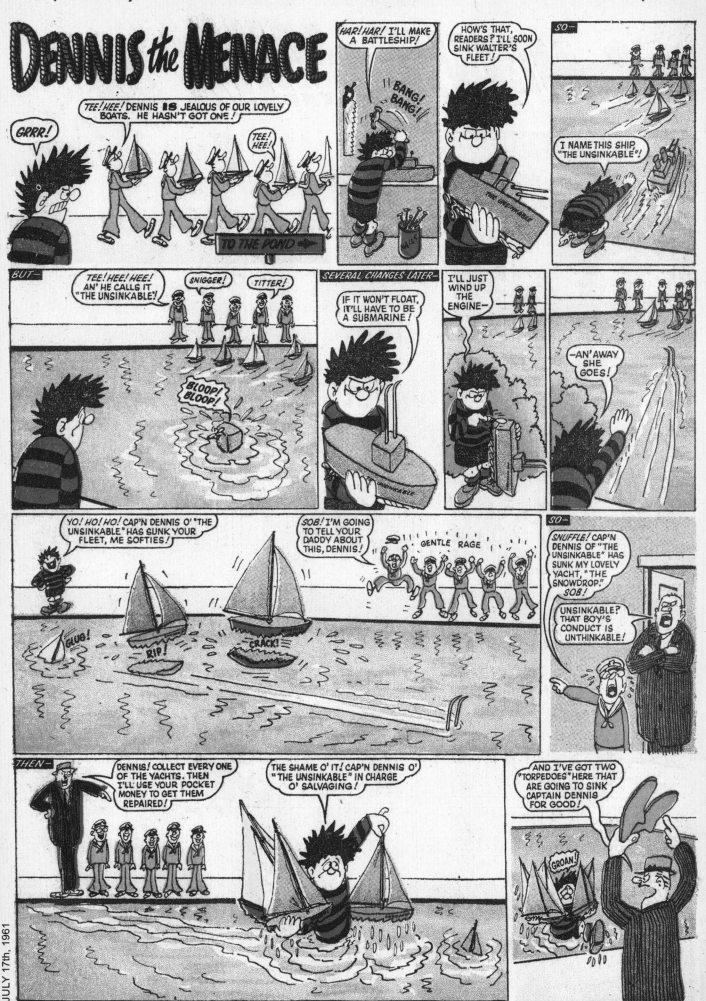

Printed and Published in Great Britain by D. C. THOMSON & Co., Ltd., and JOHN LENG & Co., Ltd., © D. C. THOMSON & CO., LTD., 1963.
12 Fetter Lane, Fleet Street, London, E.C.4. Registered for transmission by Canadian Magazine Post.

JULY 17th, 1961

Printed and Published in Great Britain by D. C. THOMSON & Co., Ltd., and JOHN LENG & Co., Ltd., © D. C. THOMSON & CO., LTD., 1963.
12 Fetter Lane, Fleet Street, London, E.C.4. Registered for transmission by Canadian Magazine Post.

Printed and Published in Great Britain by D. C. THOMSON & Co., Ltd., and JOHN LENG & Co., Ltd., 12 Fetter Lane, Fleet Street, London, E.C.4.
© D. C. THOMSON & CO., LTD., 1963.

Dennis the MENACE

Printed and Published in Great Britain by D. C. THOMSON & Co., Ltd., 12 Fetter Lane, Fleet Street, London, E.C.4.
© D C THOMSON & Co. Ltd., 1968.

Printed and Published in Great Britain by D. C. THOMSON & Co., Ltd., 12 Fetter Lane, Fleet Street, London, E.C.4. © D. C. THOMSON & CO., LTD., 1969.

Printed and Published in Great Britain by D. C. THOMSON & Co., Ltd., 12 Fetter Lane, Fleet Street, London, E.C.4.
© D. C. THOMSON & CO., LTD., 1969.

Printed and Published in Great Britain by D. C. THOMSON & Co., Ltd., 12 Fetter Lane, Fleet Street, London, E.C.4.
© D. C. THOMSON & CO., LTD., 1969.

Printed and Published in Great Britain by D. C. THOMSON & Co., Ltd., 12 Fetter Lane, Fleet Street, London, E.C.4.
© D. C. THOMSON & CO., LTD., 1970.

DENNIS the MENACE AND GNASHER

Printed and Published in Great Britain by D. C. THOMSON & Co., Ltd., 12 Fetter Lane, Fleet Street, London, E.C.4.
© D. C. THOMSON & CO., LTD., 1970.

Printed and Published in Great Britain by D. C. THOMSON & Co., Ltd., 12 Fetter Lane, Fleet Street, London, E.C.4.

The BEANO

FREE INSIDE—"THE HAPPY HOWLER" SIREN!

No. 1678—SEP. 14th, 1974.   EVERY THURSDAY   3p

Printed and Published in Great Britain by D. C. THOMSON & CO., LTD., 12 Fetter Lane, Fleet Street, London, EC4A 1BL.
© D. C. THOMSON & CO., LTD., 1974.

THE BEANO

The Comic With "BABY-FACE" FINLAYSON!

No. 1720—JULY 5th, 1975.   EVERY THURSDAY   4p

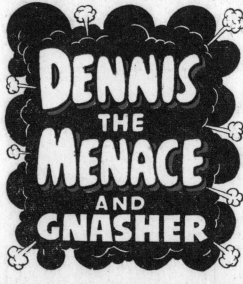

DENNIS THE MENACE AND GNASHER

MORE ON BACK PAGE

THE BEANO

The Comic With THE BASH ST. KIDS!

No. 1729—SEPT. 6th, 1975.　　EVERY THURSDAY　　4p

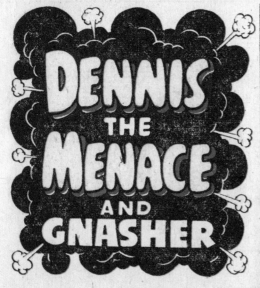

DENNIS THE MENACE AND GNASHER

HEY! LOOK AT THAT ARMY MASCOT, GNASHER!

YOU'RE MY MASCOT, SO I'D BETTER MAKE SURE YOU HAVE A PROPER MASCOT UNIFORM.

SHOULD HAVE THE VERY THING HERE.

THERE—THAT OLD JERSEY OF MINE MAKES A FINE UNIFORM!

NOW FOR SOME DRILL LIKE THE SOLDIERS DO—ATTENTION!

CLICK!　CLICK!

QUICK MARCH!

MORE ON BACK PAGE.

Printed and Published in Great Britain by D. C. THOMSON & CO., LTD., 185 Fleet Street, London, EC4A 2HS.

THE BEANO

The Comic With ROGER the DODGER !

No. 1737—NOV. 1st, 1975. EVERY THURSDAY 4p

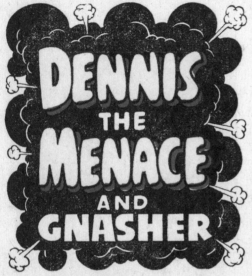

MORE ON BACK PAGE.

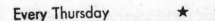

DENNIS the MENACE AND GNASHER
CONTINUED FROM FRONT PAGE.

Printed and Published in Great Britain by D. C. THOMSON & CO., LTD., 185 Fleet Street, London, EC4A 2HS.

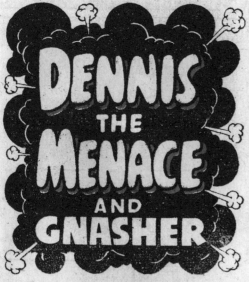

DENNIS THE MENACE AND GNASHER

HAMMER! THUMP! BANG! CLANG!

DENNIS'S HUT

THE SOFTIES HAVE CHALLENGED US TO A WATER-PISTOL FIGHT...

...AND WE'RE REALLY GOING TO DELUGE THEM!

GURGLE!

LET'S TRY IT OUT — JUMP ON THE WATER CONTAINER, GNASHER.

DUMMY SOFTIE

GNESH!

SPACE HOPPER

SO—

BOUNCE!

SPACE HOPPER

TRICKLE

WE'LL NEED MORE WEIGHT ON THIS THING. BY THE WAY, WHERE'S GNASHER?

GURGLE!

SPACE HOPPER

TAP! TAP!

OOPS! SORRY, OLD PAL — WE'LL GET YOU DOWN!

MORE ON BACK PAGE.

DENNIS the MENACE AND GNASHER
CONTINUED FROM FRONT PAGE.

Printed and Published in Great Britain by D. C. THOMSON & CO., LTD., 185 Fleet Street, London, EC4A 2HS.

THE BEANO

GET A GNASHER BADGE! *SEE PAGE 9*

No. 1845—NOV. 26th, 1977.   EVERY THURSDAY   5p

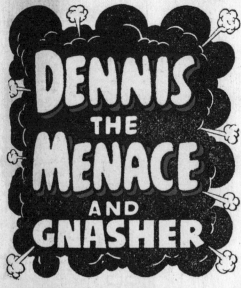

DENNIS THE MENACE AND GNASHER

THE SCHOOL IS GOING PONY-TREKKING TOMORROW!

GOODY!   ← SOFTIES' CHORUS

THE BADDIES ARE PLEASED, TOO—

WINK

NEXT DAY—

WHERE'S DENNIS? AND CURLY? AND PIEFACE?

TEACHER

HERE WE ARE, MARSHAL!

HOWDY!

I'M RIN TIN CAN!

MORE ON BACK PAGE.

Printed and Published in Great Britain by D. C. THOMSON & CO., LTD., 185 Fleet Street, London, EC4A 2HS.

THE BEANO

40 YEARS OF FUN

"FIRST" BEANO JULY 30th 1938

No. 1880 — JULY 29th, 1978

EVERY THURSDAY

5p

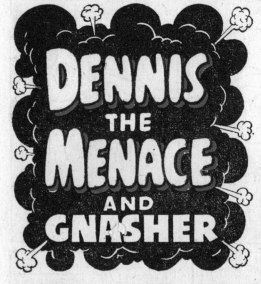

DENNIS THE MENACE AND GNASHER

WAHEY! IT'S MY BIRTHDAY!

GNEEK!

WONDER WHAT'S IN MY PARCELS?

TO DENNIS

TO DENNIS

TO DENNIS

A WATER-PISTOL FROM CURLY, A PEA-SHOOTER FROM PIE-FACE, AND A COWBOY SUIT FROM GRANNY!

PEAS

AND WHERE DO YOU THINK YOU'RE GOING?

OUT, DAD — TO PLAY WITH THESE!

BUT— YOU'RE GOING NOWHERE UNTIL YOU'VE WRITTEN YOUR "THANK-YOU" LETTERS!

OH, ALL RIGHT!

GNO FUN!

MORE ON BACK PAGE.

Printed and Published in Great Britain by D. C. THOMSON & CO., LTD., 185 Fleet Street, London, EC4A 2HS.

THE BEANO

WIN A DENNIS JERSEY

SEE PAGE NINE!

No. 1920—MAY 5th, 1979   EVERY THURSDAY   6p

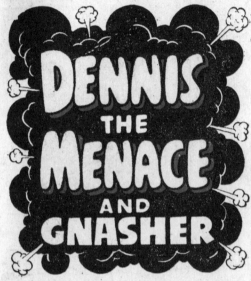

DENNIS THE MENACE AND GNASHER

GRUNT! NOT NEARLY REVOLTING ENOUGH SWILL THAT!

SNIFF!

HA-HA! WHAT A FINE PORKER!

SPLAT!

PLONK!

PESKY MENACE — WISH I COULD GET RID OF IT!

I'LL TAKE HIM OFF YOUR HANDS!

NOW I HAVE TWO PETS — GNASHER AND RASHER!

GNASH!

GRUNT!

TRA-LA! I'M OFF TO GET MY DEAR LITTLE PIGGY-BANK OPENED!

SOFTY WALTER

SKIP

YAROOP!

NICE OF RASHER TO HELP YOU OPEN YOUR BANKIE, WALTER!

HOINK! HOINK!

CRUNCH!

BOO-HOO! WHAT A FRIGHTFUL BOAR!

MORE ON BACK PAGE

Printed and Published in Great Britain by D.C. THOMSON & CO., LTD.,185 Fleet Street, London, EC4A 2HS.

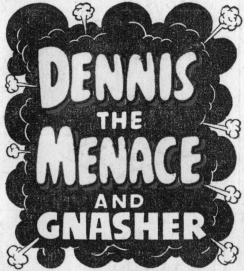

Printed and Published in Great Britain by D.C. THOMSON & CO., LTD., 185 Fleet Street, London, EC4A 2HS.

THE BEANO

No. 1981—JULY 5th, 1980   EVERY THURSDAY   **7p**

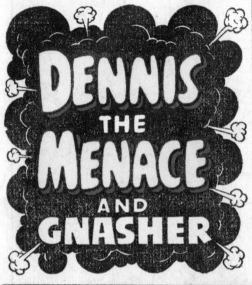

DENNIS THE MENACE AND GNASHER

WALTER THE SOFT BOY

FOO-FOO THE SOFT DOG

IT'S NO GOOD, FOO-FOO, DEAR— THERE'S NOTHING ELSE FOR IT...

...YOU'LL HAVE TO STAY AT DENNIS'S HOUSE WHILE WE'RE AWAY FOR THE WEEKEND!

WHIMPER!

DENNIS'S HOUSE

DON'T WORRY—I'LL LOOK AFTER THE LITTLE DARLING.

BE A GOOD LITTLE DOGGIE FOR THE NICE LADY.

BAH!

GRR!

Presently—

MMM! WHAT A LOVELY COOKING SMELL!

WAFT

NICE NIFF

YUM-YUM!

GNUM-GNUM!

HANDS OFF! THAT'S NOT FOR YOU!

SMACK!

SMACK!

IT'S FOR SWEET LITTLE FOO-FOO! YOU CAN ALWAYS OPEN A TIN OF BEANS!

POLITE DROOL!

MORE ON BACK PAGE.

Printed and Published in Great Britain by D. C. THOMSON & CO., LTD.,185 Fleet Street, London, EC4A 2HS

THE BEANO

IT'S FAN-TASTIC! WHAT IS? SEE PAGE NINE

No. 1989—AUG. 30th, 1980   EVERY THURSDAY   8p

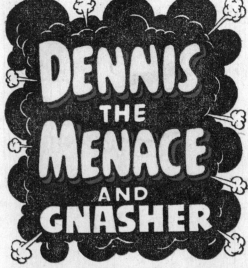

MORE ON BACK PAGE

Printed and Published in Great Britain by D.C. THOMSON & CO., LTD.,185 Fleet Street, London, EC4A 2HS.

THE BEANO

MY CLUB NEEDS YOU!

SEE PAGE 9

DENNIS the MENACE FAN CLUB

No. 1994—OCT. 4th, 1980   EVERY THURSDAY   8p

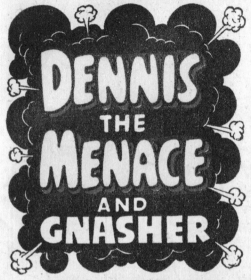

DENNIS THE MENACE AND GNASHER

It's the apple season—

I'M READY FOR YOU THIS YEAR!

GOOD WORK, GNASHER!

SHAKE

GRR! I'LL HAVE TO TRY SOMETHING ELSE!

MY BROTHER'S A GUARDSMAN! THE MENACES WON'T GET PAST HIM!

But—

EEK!

MORE ON BACK PAGE

THE BEANO

WIN A **DENNIS JERSEY**
SEE PAGE 9

No. 1964—MARCH 8th, 1980   EVERY THURSDAY   **7p**

DENNIS the MENACE FAN CLUB

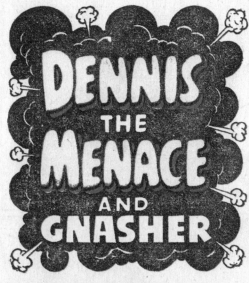

DENNIS THE MENACE AND GNASHER

MORE ON BACK PAGE

DENNIS the MENACE AND GNASHER
CONTINUED FROM FRONT PAGE

Printed and Published in Great Britain by D. C. THOMSON & CO., LTD.,185 Fleet Street, London, EC4A 2HS

THE BEANO

MY CLUB NEEDS YOU!

SEE PAGE 9

DENNIS the MENACE FAN CLUB

No. 1972—MAY 3rd, 1980   EVERY THURSDAY   7p

DENNIS THE MENACE AND GNASHER

RIGHT, DENNIS — READ TO ME FROM YOUR POETRY BOOK.

ER — "THE BOY STOOD ON THE BURNING DUCK..."

DECK NOT DUCK! YOUR READING IS ATROCIOUS!

At four o'clock —

TRING!

I WANT YOU TO PRACTISE READING OUT LOUD!

HUH! SOME CHANCE!

On his way home —

NEWSAGENT

BOY WANTED FOR MORNING PAPER ROUND

Early next morning —

ENT

THIS IS A GREAT JOB...

...IT MEANS I CAN GET AN EARLY READ OF "THE BEANO"!

GNASHEE!

HAR-HAR! DON'T MIND THIS SORT TO READING!

MORE ON BACK PAGE

THE BEANO

No. 2122—MARCH 19th, 1983   EVERY THURSDAY   10p (R 15p Inc. VAT)

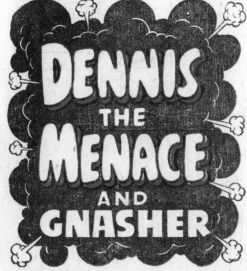

MORE ON BACK PAGE

Printed and Published in Great Britain by D. C. THOMSON & CO., LTD.,185 Fleet Street, London EC4A 2HS.

THE BEANO

JON GNASHER'S FANG CLUB SEE PAGE 9

No. 2136—JUNE 25th, 1983   EVERY THURSDAY   10p
I.R.14½p (Inc. VAT)

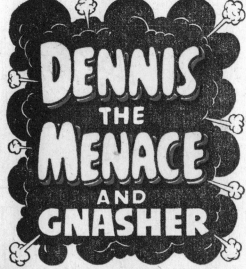

DENNIS THE MENACE AND GNASHER

HMM! YOU GET "MOTHER'S DAY" AND "FATHER'S DAY"... I WONDER..?

WHISPER, WHISPER!

WHAT'S DENNIS UP TO?

Next morning-

WHERE ARE THEY?

BUMP!

YEOWP!

SHOVE

PRACTICE SWING

WHERE ARE WHAT, DENNIS?

TUG

MY "SON'S DAY" CARDS AND PRESENTS—DON'T TELL ME YOU'VE FORGOTTEN!

HADN'T HEARD ABOUT THIS!

Later-

LOOK WHAT WE GOT FROM OUR PARENTS!

GULP! DENNIS MUST BE RIGHT ABOUT THIS "SON'S DAY"!

I'LL GIVE HIM MY BEST CHOCOLATES.

I'LL FAKE UP THIS "FATHER'S DAY" CARD.

SILENT MIRTH!

CLEVER - VERY CLEVER!

CHOCS

SON FOR YOU DAD ON YOUR SPECIAL DAY

MORE ON BACK PAGE

Printed and Published in Great Britain by D. C. THOMSON & CO., LTD., 185 Fleet Street, London EC4A 2HS.

THE BEANO

2 SUPER BADGES for EVERY MEMBER!

see page 9

DENNIS the MENACE FAN CLUB

No. 2152—OCT. 15th, 1983   EVERY THURSDAY   12p
I.R. 17½p (Inc. VAT)

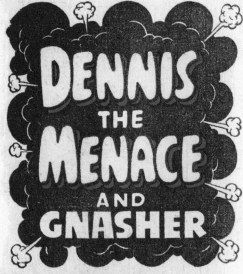

DENNIS THE MENACE AND GNASHER

MORE ON BACK PAGE

Printed and Published in Great Britain by D. C. THOMSON & CO., LTD., 185 Fleet Street, London EC4A 2HS.

THE BEANO

No. 2161—DEC. 17th, 1983   EVERY THURSDAY   12p
I.R. 18p (inc. VAT)

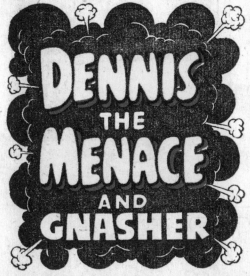

DENNIS THE MENACE AND GNASHER

MORE ON BACK PAGE

Printed and Published in Great Britain by D. C. THOMSON & CO., LTD.,185 Fleet Street, London EC4A 2HS.

THE BEANO

No. 2166—JAN. 21st, 1984   EVERY THURSDAY   12p
I.R. 20p (Inc. VAT)

MY CLUB NEEDS YOU!

SEE PAGE 9

DENNIS the MENACE FAN CLUB

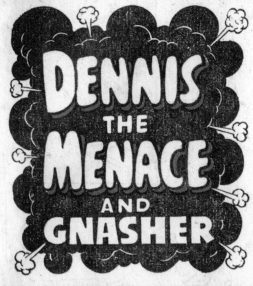

DENNIS THE MENACE AND GNASHER

IT WILL BE VERY COLD TONIGHT.

OOH! I'D BETTER SEE HOW GNASHER'S DOING.

POOR OLD GNASHER— HE'S FREEZING!

S-H-A-K-E

SHAKE

CHATTER!

CHATTER!

COLLAPSE

ERK! HE'S BEEN SHAKING SO MUCH THE KENNEL'S COLLAPSED!

GNASHER

PSST! IN YOU COME, GNASHER... MUM WILL NEVER KNOW.

CHATTER! CHATTER!

So—

ZOOM!

But—

SUSPICIOUS

HMM!

OUT!

MORE ON BACK PAGE

Printed and Published in Great Britain by D. C. THOMSON & CO., LTD.,185 Fleet Street, London EC4A 2HS.

THE BEANO

SUPER DENNIS POSTERS TO BE WON—SEE PAGE 9.

No. 2213—DECEMBER 15th, 1984   EVERY THURSDAY   14p
I.R. 23p (Inc. VAT)

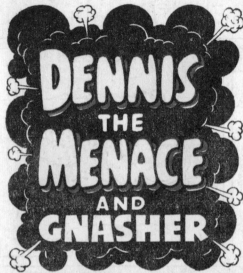

MORE ON BACK PAGE

Printed and Published in Great Britain by D. C. THOMSON & CO., LTD., 185 Fleet Street, London EC4A 2HS.

THE BEANO

2 SUPER BADGES for EVERY MEMBER!

see page 8

No. 2279 MARCH 22nd, 1986.

EVERY THURSDAY

16p
I.R. 26p
(inc. VAT)

MORE ON BACK PAGE

Printed and Published in Great Britain by D. C. Thomson & Co. Ltd., 185 Fleet Street, London EC4A 2HS.

THE BEANO

GNASHER'S BACK!

No. 2286 MAY 10th, 1986　　EVERY THURSDAY　　16p

I.R. 26p (inc. VAT)

MORE ON BACK PAGE

Printed and Published in Great Britain by D. C. Thomson & Co. Ltd., 185 Fleet Street, London EC4A 2HS.
© D. C. Thomson & Co. Ltd., 1986.

THE BEANO

WITH A FREE DENNIS ANNIVERSARY POSTER

No. 2539 MARCH 16th, 1991.

EVERY THURSDAY **26p**

DENNIS the MENACE 40 Menacing Years and Gnasher

DROP IN ON THE BACK PAGE FOR SOME PARTY FUN!

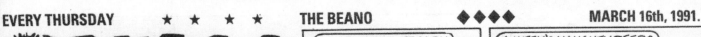

Printed and Published in Great Britain by D. C. THOMSON & CO., LTD., 185 Fleet Street, London, EC4A 2HS.

THE BEANO

No. 2540 MARCH 23rd, 1991.

EVERY THURSDAY **26p**

DENNIS *the* MENACE FAN CLUB

JOIN DENNIS'S FAN CLUB—SEE INSIDE FOR DETAILS!

THE BEANO

No. 2566 SEPTEMBER 21st 1991   EVERY THURSDAY   **26p**

HOW TO JOIN? FIND OUT INSIDE!

THE  Super COMPETITION INSIDE !

BEANO

No. 2731 NOVEMBER 19th 1994   EVERY THURSDAY 38p

DENNIS the MENACE and GNASHER

GASP! DAD'S SELLING GNASHER BECAUSE OF THINGS IN THE HOUSE BEING CHEWED!

GLOOM

DOG FOR SALE

GNASHER

GNUMPH!

I'M GOING BACK TO MY BED. MAYBE THIS IS A BAD DREAM AND I'LL SOON WAKE UP TO FIND OUT IT ISN'T TRUE!

PUSH

G...GASP!

THE BEANO

No. 2817 JULY 13th 1996

EVERY THURSDAY 40p

DENNIS the MENACE and GNASHER

WHAT'LL WE DO TODAY, GNASHER?

9 770262 246065

WHAT'S THIS?
SHAKE
IT'S MOVING!
SHAKE
LIFT
GNASHER! I SUPPOSE DEEP SNOW AND SHORT LEGS DON'T MIX!
GNUMPH!
WAH! I'D BETTER HEAT YOU UP BEFORE YOU DEAFEN ME!
GNBRRRRRRRR!
VERY LOUD CHATTERING OF TEETH
COME ON INSIDE MY JUMPER! IT'LL KEEP US BOTH WARM! HO-HO!
GNAHA!
LEAP
JEWELLERS
ALSO HANDY FOR . . .
PIZZA PLACE
NO DOGS ALLOWED
GIANT PIZZAS
. . . SNEAKING GNASHER INTO THE PIZZA PLACE!
EH?
WAASSAT?
GNASH! GUZZLE!
MUNCH! CHOMP!
AAAGH! A TWO HEADED MENACE MONSTER!
GNASHEE! CHOMP!
HA-HA! TWO HEADS ARE BETTER THAN ONE!

To help with publicity around the time of his 50th birthday, this spoof strip, telling the origin of the striped jumper, was created. Drawn by David Parkins in the style of Davey Law, it was never published in the comic or annual.

JUNE 8th, 2002

BNO.8.6.02

BNO.8.6.02

DENNIS the MENACE and GNASHER

AUGUST 27th, 2005

DENNIS the MENACE and GNASHER

OCTOBER 29th, 2005

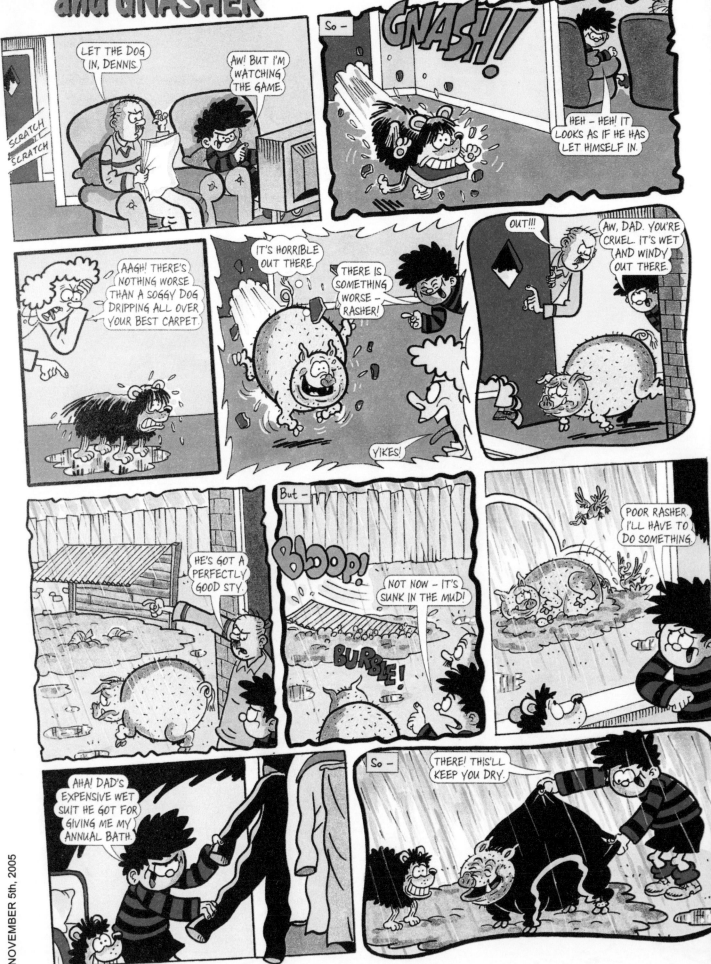

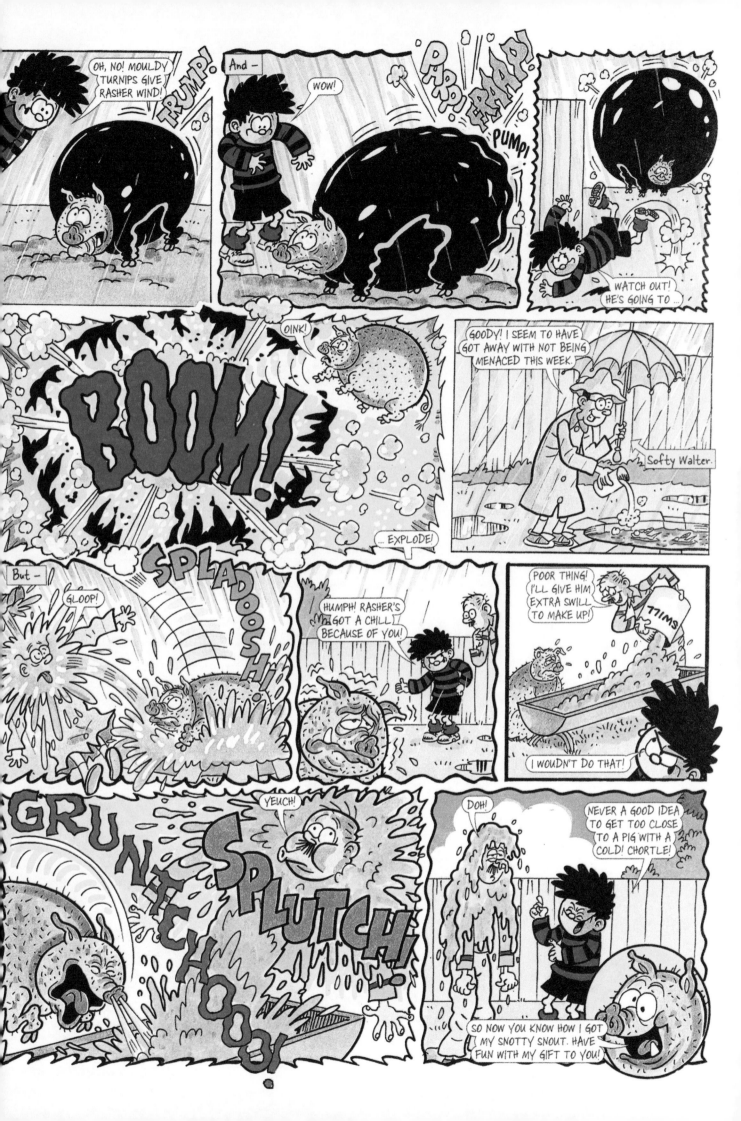

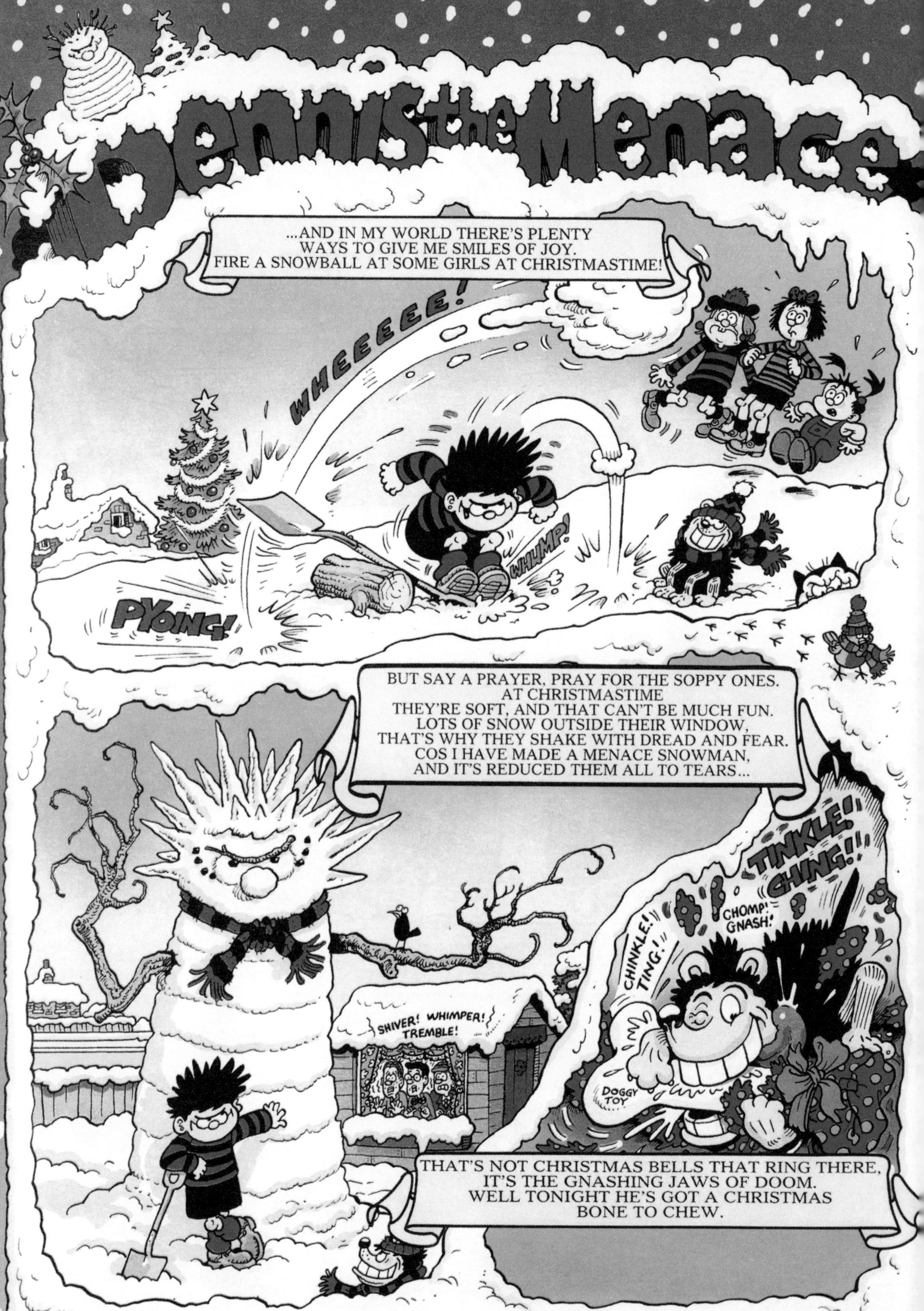

DECEMBER 26th, 2005

JANUARY 31st, 2009

WHAT'S BIG, HAIRY AND GOES UP AND DOWN?   A YETI ON A POGO STICK!

DENNIS the MENACE AND GNASHER

WHAT'S A FROG'S FAVOURITE FLOWER? THE CROAKUS!

Dennis and Gnasher

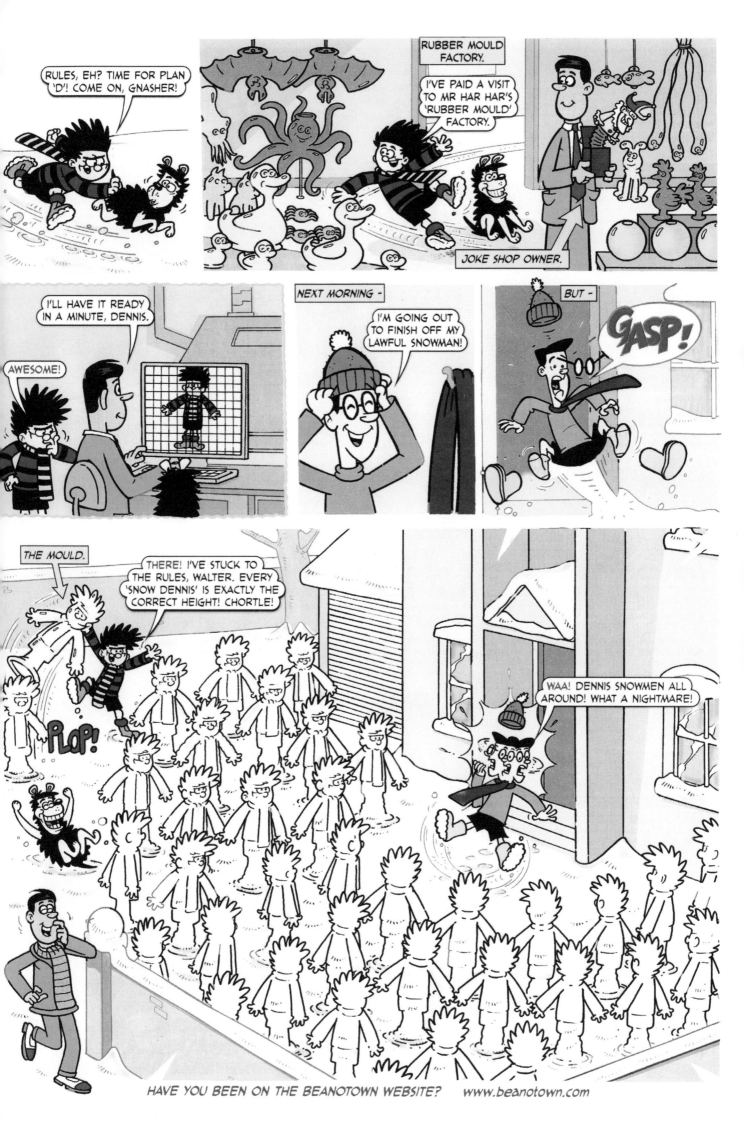

DENNIS & GNASHER

THE WORLD'S WILDEST BOY... AND HIS BEST FRIEND!

URRGH! THIS ISN'T FAIR, GNASHER. FOR HOMEWORK I'VE GOT TO WRITE...

...A STORY!

USING VERBS!

IT'S TAKING AGES! HOW MUCH HAVE I DONE SO FAR?

ARRGH! STILL NOTHING!

TWO WORDS – BOR-ING!

AND I'VE FORGOTTEN WHAT A VERB IS.

MUM! WHAT'S A VERB?!

A DOING WORD!

RAN, JUMPED, LAUGHED, HOPPED!

'SHOUTED' IN THE SENTENCE, 'MUM SHOUTED FROM DOWNSTAIRS'!

THE WORD 'WROTE' IN THE SENTENCE, 'DENNIS WROTE THE WORLD'S MOST AWESOME STORY!'

DEN MENACESON WALKED OUT... NO, NOT WALKED – EXPLODED! DEN MENACESON EXPLODED OUT OF HIS OFFICE AND RAN... NO, CRASHED DOWN THE STAIRS AS THE ALIEN GNASH SNAKED AFTER HIM!

WAIT! AM I THE BADDIE?

WHAT'S AN EXCITING VERB TO GET OUT ONTO THE STREET, GNASHER?

GNASH!

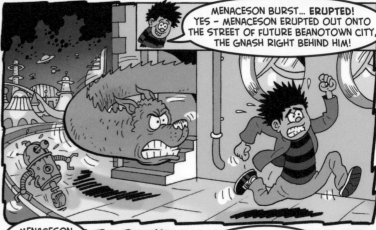

MENACESON BURST... ERUPTED! YES – MENACESON ERUPTED OUT ONTO THE STREET OF FUTURE BEANOTOWN CITY, THE GNASH RIGHT BEHIND HIM!

WHAT'S A COOLER WORD THAN 'RUN'? SOMETHING FAST! USAIN BOLT IS FAST, ISN'T HE?

MENACESON USAINED DOWN THE ROAD, HOPING TO LOSE THE GNASH IN THE PARK.

BEANO CITY ONE

PARK

HE KANGAROOED THE RAILINGS AND... HID. NAH! HE KANGAROOED THE FENCE AND GHOSTED INTO THE BUSHES!

WORDS: NIGEL AUCHTERLOUNIE ART: NIGEL PARKINSON APRIL 12th 2017

DENNIS & GNASHER

THE WORLD'S WILDEST BOY... AND HIS BEST FRIEND!

WORDS: NIGEL AUCHTERLOUNIE ART: NIGEL PARKINSON   MAY 31st 2017

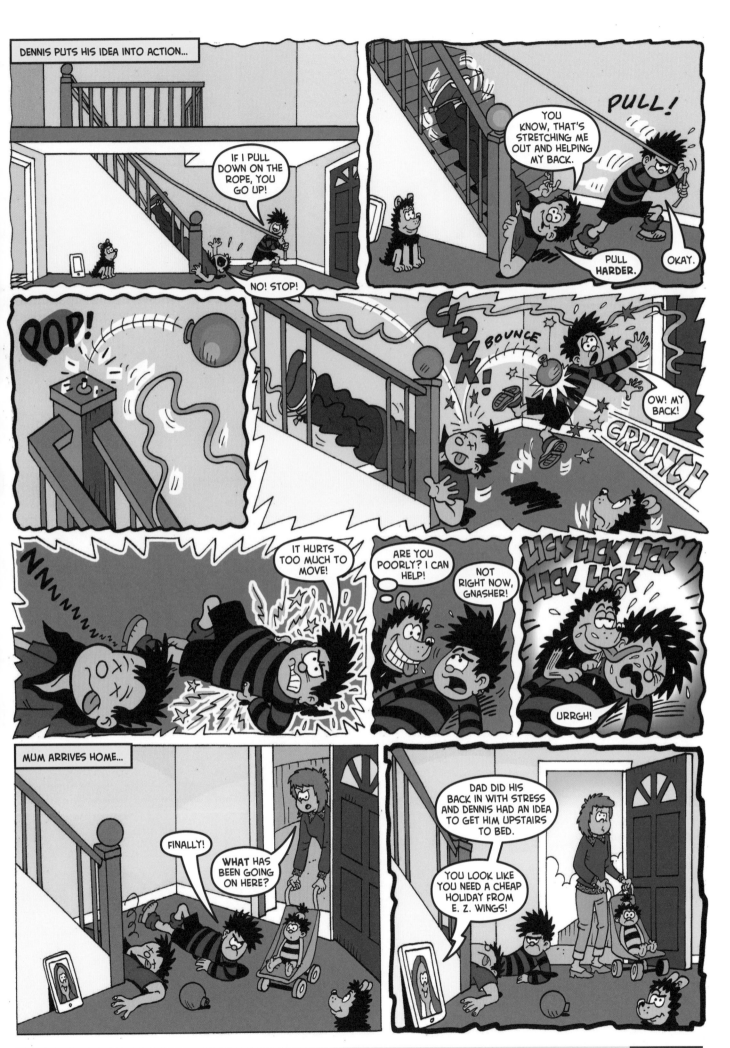

SHOPPING? THAT'S A BIT HARSH!

MOVING ON...

...TO THIS TALE OF SPOOKINESS FROM VICTORIAN TIMES WHEN KIDS WERE ON PLAYSTATION ONE AND PHONES HAD BUTTONS!

BUTTONS? ON PHONES?! I'M ALREADY UNNERVED!

IT'S A STORY I LIKE TO CALL...

THE HOUND OF THE BASHERVILLES!

I WAS AT HOME IN 221B BEANO STREET WITH MY GOOD FRIEND, THE FAMOUS DETECTIVE SHEERLUCK BONES...

DENNIS, YOU'RE MEANT TO WRITE DOWN MY INVESTIGATIONS...

...AND IN 148 SUCCESSFUL CASES, I'VE GNEVER SEEN YOU PUT PEN TO PAPER ONCE!

WHO'S A GOOD BOY?

UMM... I, ER...

...LOOK! A LETTER FROM LORD BASHERVILLE! IT SAYS TO COME AT ONCE!

To Sheerluck Bones

Dear Mr Bones
HELP!
Come at once!

Yours,
Lord Basherville

WORDS: NIGEL AUCHTERLOUNIE ART: NIGEL PARKINSON OCTOBER 25th, 2017

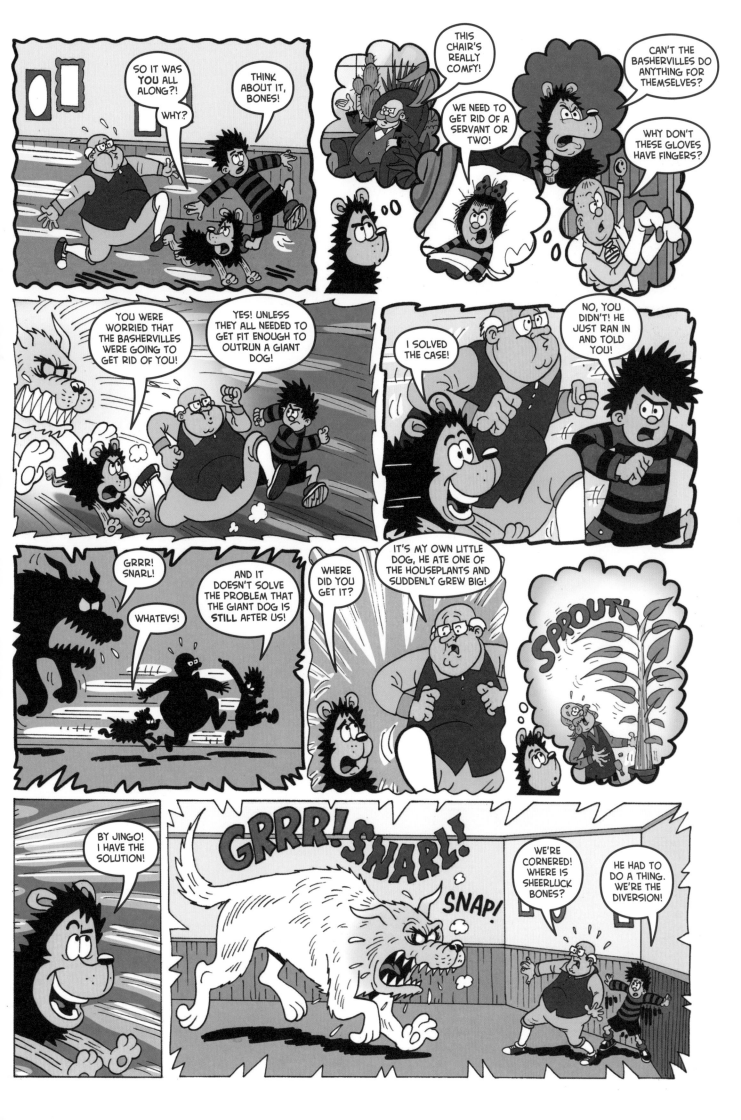

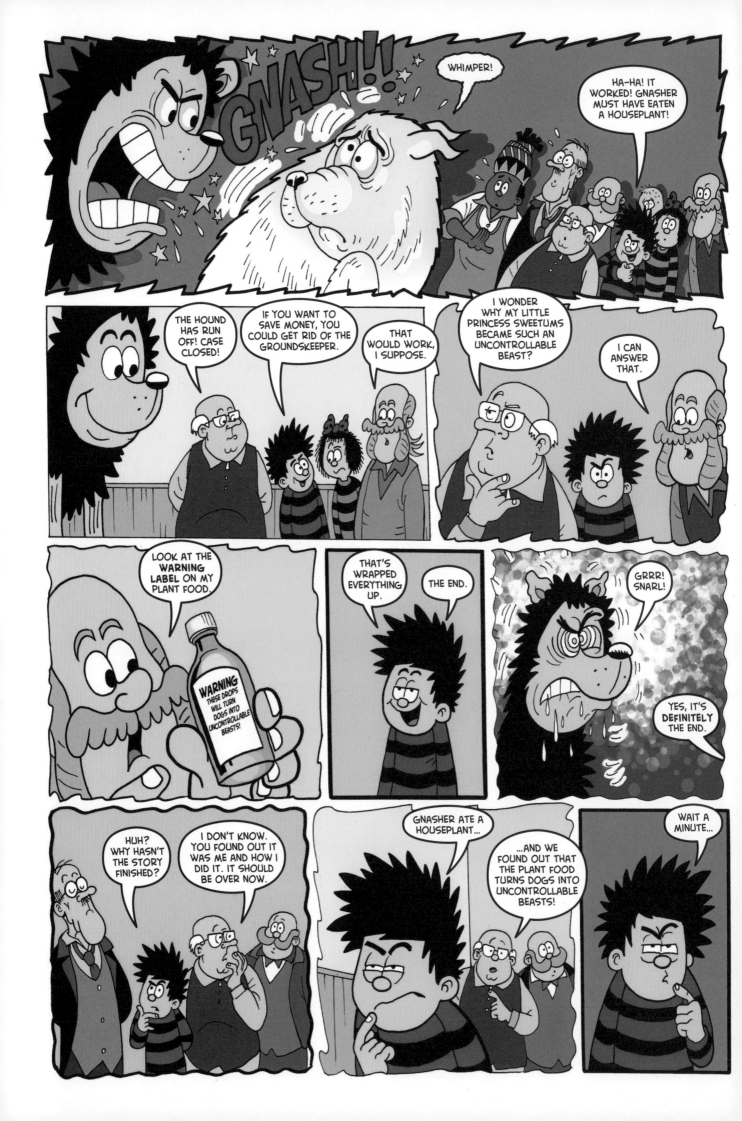

THE OTHER HOUND OF THE BASHERVILLES!

GNASH!
GNASH!
GNASH!

...ARRGH!

THE END!

I LIKE HOW YOU LEFT IT OPEN FOR A SEQUEL.

I LIKED THE BIT WHERE I'M GOING TO GNASH EVERYONE!

DENNIS HAS FOUND MUM'S OLD PHONE AND IS PLAYING SOMETHING CALLED 'SNAKE'...

HOW CAN I LIKE THIS? IT ONLY HAS TWO COLOURS!

...WHILE SKATING.

BACKWARDS!

CLOSED BY ORDER OF THE MAYOR

C[...] [...] THE M[...]

JUST A MOMENT...

...ARRGH!

SHUT DOWN

THE MAYOR SAYS CLOSED!

OH GNO!

NO ENTRY

NIGEL PARKINSON

WORDS: NIGEL AUCHTERLOUNIE ART: NIGEL PARKINSON NOVEMBER 1st, 2017

IN ...TOO LATE TO SKATE!

AT THE MAYOR'S OFFICE...

WHAT'S GOING ON? WH[...] HAVE YOU SHUT O[...] SKATEPARK?!

MAYO[...]

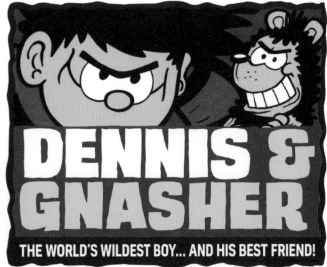

DENNIS & GNASHER

THE WORLD'S WILDEST BOY... AND HIS BEST FRIEND!

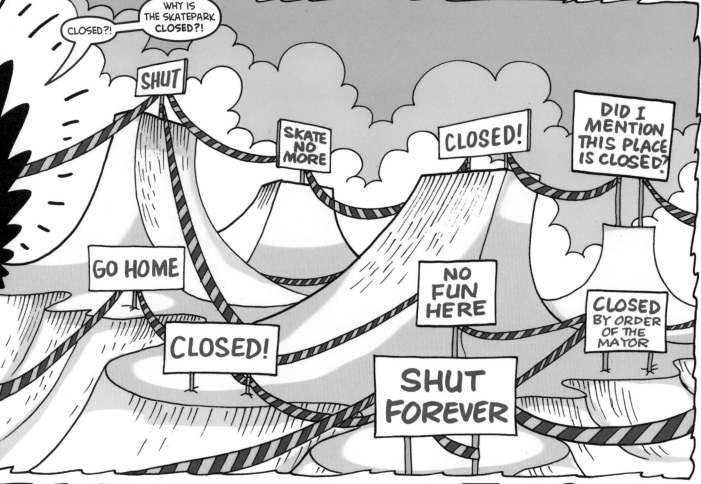

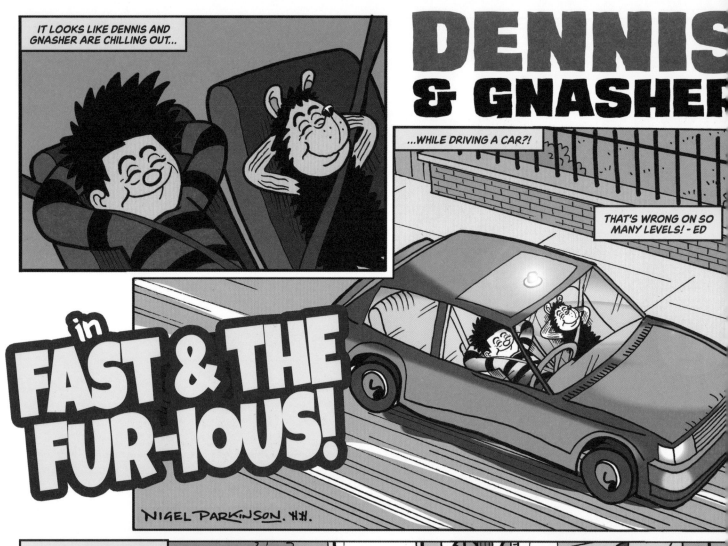

IT LOOKS LIKE DENNIS AND GNASHER ARE CHILLING OUT...

DENNIS & GNASHER

...WHILE DRIVING A CAR?!

THAT'S WRONG ON SO MANY LEVELS! - ED

in FAST & THE FUR-IOUS!

NIGEL PARKINSON. HH.

EARLIER, AT BEANOTOWN TOWN SQUARE...

WHAT'S THIS?

DRIVE TO THE FUTURE!

LET ME EXPLAIN.

WE OFFER TWO TYPES OF CAR...

...THE *CLASSIC* DUAL-DRIVE THAT STILL HAS A STEERING WHEEL...

...AND THE *LATEST* PROTOTYPE WITHOUT.

NOW ON LONG JOURNEYS, YOU CAN SIT BACK AND PASS THE TIME CHATTING FACE TO FACE.

CHAT?! NO THANKS! WE'L STICK WITH TH CLASSIC.

WORDS: Nigel Auchterlounie ART: Nigel Parkinson APRIL 10th, 2019

THE WORLD'S WILDEST BOY... AND HIS BEST FRIEND!

WATCH OUT FOR THAT HOLE, DENNIS! - ED

SWERVE!

ROADWORKS AHEAD

ARE WE THERE YET?

DUNNO! I'VE GOT MY EYES CLOSED!

JUST WHAT IS GOING ON?! - ED

BEANOTOWN IS GOING TO BE THE *FIRST* TOWN IN THE COUNTRY TO ALLOW COMPUTER-CONTROLLED, SELF-DRIVING CARS ON ITS ROADS.

WHY?

TO EMBRACE THE FUTURE!

YEAH, BUT REALLY, WHY?

MAYOR BROWN, WHERE WOULD YOU LIKE ME TO LEAVE THE *MONEY* FOR LETTING US TEST OUR CARS IN YOUR TOWN?

HOW MUCH IS IT?

IF IT'S MORE THAN *SOME* MONEY, I CAN'T AFFORD IT.

'SOME'?!

HOW DOES IT WORK?

JUST TALK TO IT.

DENNIS & GNASHER

THE WORLD'S WILDEST BOY... AND HIS BEST FRIEND!

THE MENACE FAMILY ARE AT A POSH RESTAURANT...

BUT *WHY*, THOUGH?

IT'S OUR *ANNIVERSARY.* HOW LONG HAVE WE BEEN MARRIED?

IT FEELS LIKE *FOREVER*, BUT IT'S PROBABLY *LESS* THAN THAT.

DID I SAY THAT *OUT LOUD?*

WHAT?! *GNASHER* CAN'T BE HERE! IT'S A POSH RESTAURANT!

AT LEAST GNASHER IS ON HIS *BEST BEHAVIOUR.*

CHILL, MUM. THAT'S WHY HE'S IN HIS *BEST TUXEDO.* NOTHING CAN GO WRONG!

ARE YOU READY TO ORDER, SIR?

YOUR SOUP AND YOUR HUGEWURST.

ENJOY, SIR.

GASP!

ER... HE'LL HAVE WHAT THEY'RE HAVING.

QUICKLY!

SAUSAGE!

ARRGH!

DRAG!

CRASH!

SPLAT!

WORDS: Nigel Auchterlounie ART: Nigel Parkinson MAY 29th, 2019

 What do cars do at parties? Brake dance!

DENNIS & GNASHER

DEEP IN BEANOTOWN WOOD, A PRICKLY BUSH RUSTLES. WHAT MANNER OF WILD CREATURE IS ABOUT TO BURST FORTH?

RUSTLE!

YOWCH!

SPIKY!

USUALLY WHEN WE GO EXPLORING, WE FIND SOMETHING AMAZING LIKE A CRYSTAL SKULL, FORGOTTEN TUNNELS, DINOSAURS, TROLLS, WITCHES, TIME MACHINES, BURIED TREASURE, GHOSTS, ZOMBIE PIRATES OR CONKERS, BUT THERE'S NOTHING TODAY!

THE DAY'S GNOT OVER YET, DENNIS!

BACK HOME...

HUH?! WHERE'S MY SLEEVE GONE?

I MUST HAVE CAUGHT IT ON A THORN.

DENNIS! MY MUM SENSE IS TINGLING! HAVE YOU DONE SOMETHING? I WON'T BE PLEASED IF IT'S *JUMPER* RELATED BECAUSE THAT'S YOUR LAST ONE!

YIKES!

I'D BETTER GATHER UP THE WOOL SO GRAN CAN FIX MY SLEEVE.

NIGEL PARKINSON

BACK IN THE WOODS, THE SAME PRICKLY BUSH RUSTLES. WHAT MANNER OF WILD CREATURE IS ABOUT TO BURST FORTH THIS TIME?

RUSTLE!

YOWCH!

SPIKY!

I THINK MY DRONE IS PROPERLY LOST!

I'LL JUST *PRETEND* I STILL HAVE IT IF MY PARENTS ASK.

WATCH IT, MINNIE! YOU'RE UNRAVELLING! - ED

WHOA! I NEVER KNEW YOU NEEDED SO MUCH WOOL TO MAKE A SLEEVE.

I THOUGHT IT'D CAUGHT ON THIS BUSH, BUT IT GOES ON AND ON!

I DON'T REMEMBER COMING THIS WAY!

THIS IS MINNIE'S HOUSE! WERE WE EVEN *HERE*?

MINNIE! WHERE'S YOUR JUMPER?!

WORDS: Nigel Auchterlounie ART: Nigel Parkinson JANUARY 8th, 2020

Did you hear about the robbery last night? Two clothes pins held up a pair of trousers!